Simplistic Statistics

A Basic Guide to the Statistical Analysis of Biological Data

by

Lucy A Tucker BSc, PhD

Chalcombe Publications

First published in the United Kingdom by
Chalcombe Publications
Painshall, Church Lane, Welton
Lincoln LN2 3LT
United Kingdom

© L A Tucker 2003

ISBN 0 948617 43 8

CONTENTS

INTRODUCTION

First of all let me put my cards on the table. I am not a mathematician, philosopher or statistician. I am merely one of the multitude of people who have to use statistics as part of their scientific work on a regular basis. This booklet will no doubt be hated by all those professing to be statistics experts, and I make the plea now – if you are one of these people please do not bother reading further. You will not appreciate the simplifications and generalisations that I have found necessary to use as the key to the lay persons' understanding and utilisation of statistics. For all ordinary mortals, please read on.

I received a definition of statistics from a lecturer which goes as follows: "Statistics is a branch of philosophy that attempts to re-create observations by rationalisation, refinement and optimisation of data collected, that may be derived from fragments of or whole populations". Confused? Well anyone who has ever picked up a standard text on this subject knows that's how statisticians talk. They also do not seem able to agree with each other's methods or use of statistics. It's all utterly incomprehensible to the rest of us who only have GCSE Maths and just want to find out what residual variance is once and for all (and have to go through four books to find out!). Love or hate it though, statistical methods are essential for investigating characteristics of data by analysis of results obtained from experimental samples. Also, more commonly for life scientists, statistics has to be applied when comparing experimental results (the hunt for those 'significant' effects), where different 'treatments' are applied to subjects, e.g. effect of nitrogen on plant growth, effect of diet on animal growth and feeding efficiency.

The aim of compiling this book is to try to explain in normal English, with understandable and worked examples, the terms used, how basic calculations are derived and the ideas behind their formulation. Also, and arguably most importantly in a biological context, where the results come from, what they mean and if they are actually relevant to the original hypothesis. In an age where it is very simple to import a spreadsheet of data into a computer software package and press 'go', it is an important skill to spot which significant effect is biologically relevant. You will notice that I have commonly used examples from animal feeding trials, as this is my own field of interest. However the examples can be readily transposed for other disciplines where live organisms are the object of scrutiny. The sole aim of producing this book is to make people less nervous of statistics and, by applying some understanding, even in a non-mathematical way, make them think about the use and application of statistics. If you say to yourself 'Ah – I see' just once during reading, I have achieved my goal.

This book is dedicated to my parents, without whose support and encouragement I would never have been in a position to learn about and use statistics in the first place. It is also dedicated, in sympathy, to all those who have ever had to try to explain statistics to bored first year students at 9 am on a Monday morning!

I would like to thank Dr. Paul Rose, Nick Tucker, Dr. Mike Bedford and Dr. Michael Pack for their positive contribution towards my understanding of statistics over many years.

Chapter 1

DATA

A **dataset** is simply a set of data. It has a certain number of values ('observations') within it, which are denoted as '**n**' e.g. the dataset A: **1,5,3,6,9,2,8,4,5** contains 9 numbers or 'observations', so **n = 9.**

This dataset may represent anything, but for now we can suppose that it is the results of an investigation into the height, in cm, of plants in a window box. Each set of data will have a **MEAN** (average), **MEDIAN** and **MODE** value (see Chapter 2), and will also show a certain **RANGE** of values, with a fixed **DEVIATION** and **DISTRIBUTION** about its mean.

Dataset A, when arranged in order of magnitude is:

1,2,3,4,5,5,6,8,9

This is now easier to read, and we can start to look for any patterns.

The numbers in datasets are described in standard ways, depending on data type. Values of **QUANTITY** are described as **CONTINUOUS** when they are measurements that may be infinitely variable, or which have precise values which contain non-whole numbers, e.g. 7.628 cm, 55.29 kg. They may also be **DISCRETE**, whereby they are whole numbers or groups of numbers, and fractions are not appropriate, e.g. 23 eggs, 560 people (think of the nonsensical old UK family statistic 2.4 children and 0.5 of a dog per household!). Values of **QUALITY** need to be grouped as **CATEGORIES**, which may be names (**NOMINAL**), e.g. red, blue; or numbers (**ORDINAL**) e.g. years, 1992, 1993 etc. Numbers that have been grouped together in categories, or that are discrete, should be represented as bar graphs (Figure 1) or pie charts (Figure 2).

Figure 1   **Representing ordinate discrete data by bar graph**

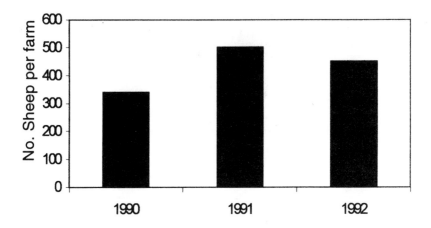

Figure 2   **Representing categories by pie chart**

Amount of maize grown by country:

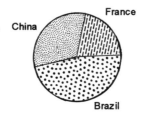

Continuous data, which is probably the most common in biological research where effects of treatments are measured, can be grouped into classes e.g. plant height values between 10 and 19 cm; 20 and 29 cm etc., but are usually represented as scatter plot graphs, as in Figure 3, where the X axis is the percentage of wheat in four diets containing different proportions of wheat, and the Y axis is the weight of groups of chickens given the diets.

Figure 3   Representing continuous data by XY scatter plot

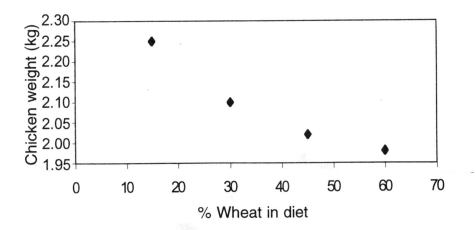

Chapter 2

MEAN, MEDIAN AND MODE

The arithmetic (calculated) **MEAN** is the average value of the numbers:

e.g. **the sum of the numbers**
       n

in the example in Chapter 1 this would be

$$\frac{1+2+3+4+5+5+6+8+9}{9} = 4.8 = \frac{\Sigma x}{n}$$

Therefore the mean plant height is **4.8 cm**. The mean is commonly written in note form as '*x*'. Every single data point (or observations) in the dataset is denoted 'x'. The equation next to the result is the common way to represent this calculation in statistics where the Σ symbol means 'sum', hence, translated, this equation reads 'the sum of all the observations 'x' divided by the number of observations 'n' equals the mean '*x*'.

The **MODE** is the value that appears most often in the dataset (if you want to think of the latest 'mode' being the latest 'fashion', then the mode value is the most fashionable, popular, or most often occurring value). In the case of dataset A on page 3, there are two plants which are 5 cm tall, the rest of the values (or observations) occur only once. Therefore the most 'popular' value is 5 cm. Sometimes within datasets there is only one modal value ('unimodal'), however there may be two or more ('multimodal') where two numbers or more occur at the same highest level of frequency. A dataset may have no modal values, when no one point is repeated more than any of the others.

The **MEDIAN** is the 'central point' i.e. that value which falls in the middle of the dataset.

1,2,3,4,<u>5</u>,5,6,8,9

Once again the value of 5 cm is in the middle of the dataset. Remember that the dataset must be arranged in ascending numeric order to find the median value. If the number of values is even, then an average of the two central values will represent the median, for example if the central values are 4 and 5, then the median would be 4.5.

The **RANGE** is the 'spread' of the values. In dataset A the numbers 'range' from **1** to **9** cm, therefore the **range of the dataset = (9-1) = 8 cm.**

Now we have some basic statistical results we can use. You are probably all aware of the usefulness of the mean (or average) value of a set of numbers. But what about the others? Well, in most non-categorical statistics (unless you're into beetle counting or suchlike) they don't seem so important. Who cares what the most 'popular' length of straw was in a field trial? It's probably so close to the mean as to make no difference anyway. Well that's true, but we will see later when we discuss more about populations, that datasets do not always behave 'normally' for many reasons, and then using the median and mode can be useful for working out what happened in an experiment. First of all, in the next Chapter we will go through some simple and common statistics to clarify some ideas about how variable experimental data can be.

Chapter 3

DATA VARIABILITY

So far all these statistical measurements have been very easy to calculate. However, when we want to assess the **VARIATION** of the values in the dataset, we must use more difficult calculations. Most people have heard of the term 'standard deviation', even if they are not entirely sure what it means. It is a commonly used measure of variability within a dataset, telling us how 'disperse' the data points are from the mean.

The variation represents the numeric distance of each observation from the calculated mean value. The most obvious and simple way to do this is by subtracting the mean 'x' from each of the individual observation values 'x' in the dataset (called the 'mean absolute deviation') to determine how far each data point is from the mean.

$x - x =$ **deviation for each recorded value**

Some of the deviation values will be positive, and some negative, depending upon whether they are higher or lower than the mean. To calculate the deviation of the whole dataset we can simply add them up. However, in their current form the result would equal zero, described statistically as $\Sigma(x-x) = 0$. The Greek symbol Σ always stands for "sum" or "add together". So to remove the negative values and make all the data positive we can **TRANSFORM** the data by squaring it (which always gives a positive number) and then taking the square root of the final answer to remove the transformation. All the squared deviations from each observation must therefore be added together, and the result is called the '**SUM OF SQUARES**' or '**SS**' (written as $\Sigma(x-x)^2$). We want to determine the average or mean deviation of all the data points (observations)

from the mean, so we divide the sum of squares value by the number of observations.

$$\frac{SS}{n} = \delta \text{ (Variance or mean deviation of dataset)}$$

In order to remove the effects of squaring the data to remove the negatives we need to find the square root of the variance:

$$\sqrt{\delta} = \textbf{Standard Deviation (sd)}$$

Now it gets tricky!

More commonly, when calculating the standard deviation, a value of **n-1** is used. This is called the **DEGREES OF FREEDOM** (df) and is used in order to increase the resulting figure for variance, and thence overestimate the standard deviation (sd). The df are regarded as a built-in margin of error to allow for any mistakes incurred whilst sampling a population. In this case the n (9) plants sampled from the window box has 9-1 = **8** degrees of freedom.

It is fairly simple to calculate variance in this manner for dataset A, as there are only 9 numbers involved. We can work through it now as an example.

x - x		Squared
1 - 4.8 =	-3.8	14.44
2 - 4.8 =	-2.8	7.84
3 - 4.8 =	-1.8	3.24
4 - 4.8 =	-0.8	0.64
5 - 4.8 =	0.2	0.04
5 - 4.8 =	0.2	0.04
6 - 4.8 =	1.2	1.44
8 - 4.8 =	3.2	10.24
9 - 4.8 =	4.2	17.64
Sum of Squares (SS)		**55.56**

Variance	=	$55.56 \div 8^{1}$	=	6.95
Standard Deviation	=	$\sqrt{6.95}$	=	2.64

[1] $n - 1 = df$

There are difficulties in calculating the variance for large datasets. The sheer volume of numbers can make the whole process very laborious, so statisticians have devised a method that helps in these situations. Instead of calculating the variance of each individual value from the mean, the equivalent figure can be arrived at by using the following equation, which gives the 'CORRECTED SUM OF SQUARES' (CSS)

$$\Sigma x^{2} - \frac{(\Sigma x)^{2}}{n} = CSS$$

I know that this formula looks horrific, but it is not so difficult as it initially appears.

To break it down:

Σx^{2} is where all the values in the dataset are squared, and then added together.

$(\Sigma x)^{2}$ is where the values in the dataset are all added together, and then the <u>result</u> is squared.

The result is divided by the number of observations in order to generate an average value of the square of all the values in total.

The standard deviation is calculated in the same manner as before, as the square root of the variance δ.

Another statistic commonly used to describe the uniformity of a dataset (i.e. how far apart the data points are from each other) is the **COEFFICIENT OF VARIATION (CV)**, which is a percentage value that describes the amount of variation in the data. The lower the percentage, the more close together the data points are to each other, and vice versa.

COEFFICIENT OF VARIATION (%) $\quad = \quad \dfrac{sd}{x} \times 100$

Experiments involving biological subjects (such as barley, humans, pigs etc.) are typically assumed to have a natural background level of variation no less than 10%, plus whatever variability is then associated with experimental treatments, analytical methods and so on. However, depending on the subject and design of the experiment, the variation may be much higher. Biological experiments should be expected to show higher CV values than datasets from studies on inanimate or manufactured objects e.g. bricks!

We have covered some basic statistics that you were probably already aware of. Now we need to be able to visualise what statistics 'look like' in graphical form. This is very useful in helping to understand what these statistics are telling us about the sample we have used and how this fits with the whole (e.g. global) population. For example, did the 200 chickens we used in an experiment react to the dietary treatment we gave them in a reliable manner, so we can be sure that all similar chickens in the world will also have the same reaction? Understanding populations is the key to ensuring that we get valid, meaningful and potentially complex information from the experimental data.

Chapter 4

POPULATIONS

What do the statistics discussed so far tell us about the sample dataset or population that we wish to study? First of all, we need to define the difference between a population and a sample. We all know that the human **POPULATION** on Earth is every single human being currently alive on the planet. Obviously it is impossible to measure e.g. the height of every person on Earth, so we take a representative **SAMPLE**, from which we can estimate the characteristics of the whole population. The same holds true for every other subject you wish to study in a statistical dataset. In experiments with barley, we would use a sample (e.g. a couple of fields or trial plots) of the whole population of barley. It is important to note that sample statistics use lower case Roman and Greek letters, whereas population statistics use capital letters – this is useful for you when you're reading up on statistical methods in other books, and wonder why they change case half way through a calculation!

In order to demonstrate the use of the statistics already discussed, we need to superimpose them onto the dataset in a manner we can visualise. Figure 4 shows what any 'normally distributed' population looks like when represented graphically. This curve can be used to represent any population characteristics, for example, heights of people. There are some very short and some very tall people in every population, but the majority are clustered around the central mean value. When these values are plotted out as a graph (called a histogram) with height along the x-axis and number of individuals of that height (frequency) along the y-axis, the result will resemble the graph below (Figure 4).

Figure 4   The normal distribution curve

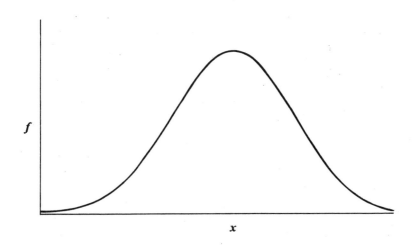

Such a population, which has equal proportions of observations above and below the mean, gives a symmetrical graph, which is referred to as the 'normal distribution' of a population. Note that the 'tails' of the curve never touch down to zero, they actually extend to infinity in either direction.

The y-axis is often denoted 'f' as it is the frequency, or number of times that the x value has been recorded. The mean of the values in a normal distribution curve is shown in Figure 5. It lies with 50% of the values of the whole population directly above and below it.

The statistics that we have calculated so far can be superimposed on this graphical representation of the population. The standard deviation (SD) describes the areas in which the individual recorded values of the dataset lie. Figure 6 shows how the SD values can be used to split up the curve of a normally distributed population.

14

Figure 5   **The mean value, represented on a normal distribution curve**

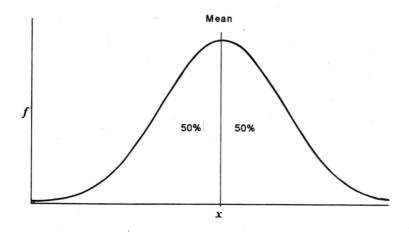

Figure 6   **Standard deviations on a normal distribution curve**

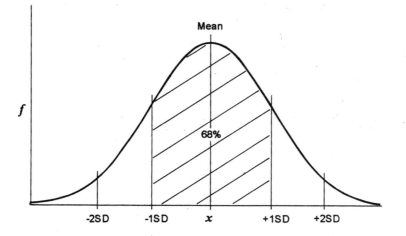

For any normally distributed population it has been calculated that 68% of all values (which corresponds to 68% of the area under the graph) will be ± 1 SD from the mean value. Therefore 1 SD corresponds with 34% (68%÷2) of all the data. This holds true no matter how large or small the dataset is, or what the mean or SD values are for that population. Correspondingly 99% of all the values in the dataset will be within ± 2.5 SD of the mean. The last 1% of all the values lie within the 'tails' of the curve. These proportions are entirely due to the mathematical characteristics of the curve that graphically describes a normally distributed population, so it is probably best to accept them and not try to work them out!

So now we can use the values calculated from the dataset to split up a population curve. What purpose does this serve regarding description of the data? Standard deviations are most commonly used to describe where an individual point lies within the dataset of the sampled population. For example, a child scored 57% in his maths test. From the mean and SD values for the whole class, we can describe whether this value was in the highest level (+ 2 SD), higher than the mean (+ 1 SD), below average (- 1 SD) or whatever. When comparing values from two different populations, e.g. the height of pygmy tribesmen versus the height of South American monks, if the population means for both populations are more than three times the SD away from each other, then the population means are likely to be significantly different.

Chapter 5

SKEWED POPULATIONS AND SAMPLING METHODS

So far we have only investigated the structure of what is referred to as a 'normally distributed population', however not all populations show this symmetry. When they are asymmetrical, this is called skewness (or 'ketosis'), the degree of which can vary. This effect will influence certain properties of the dataset. Figures 7 and 8 show examples of positive and negatively skewed populations.

Figure 7   **Positively skewed distribution curve**

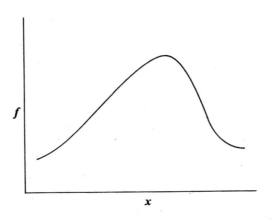

Figure 8   **Negatively skewed distribution curve**

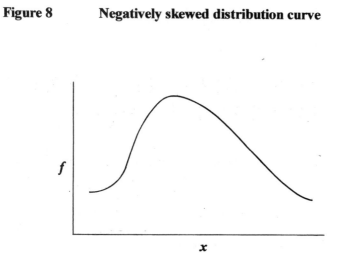

Skewed data will have a different mean, median and mode compared to normally distributed data, the range will, however, stay the same. It is important to determine whether data is skewed or not because of these changes. As we discussed earlier, comparing the mean, median and mode can be useful in determining if data is skewed, and if so by how much.

Skewed data can be caused by many things, for example a group of growing chickens may show a negative skew in data for their weight gains if they have suffered from a disease that began at a certain age, after which weight gain was depressed. This may result in the final dataset showing only a few birds attaining the expected (higher) weight gains, and disproportionately more giving lower weight gains because they have been adversely affected by disease.

Likewise, if the heights of men and women in a sample of adult humans were compared, the data as a whole (50% men, 50% women) should be normally distributed, but data for women (generally being smaller) would have a lower mean, median and mode (negative bias) and men (generally being taller) would have a higher mean, median and mode (positive bias) in comparison with the whole sample group. Therefore it would be important not to allow uneven numbers of men or women into the sample group, as this would skew the overall data. This example also illustrates the point that we must be very careful when we select our samples as being representative of whole populations, as we can inadvertently in-build bias and skewness by using data that is unbalanced.

When constructing experiments in order to create a dataset which will be statistically analysed, it is important that all the groups or samples studied are of adequate size, and that the individuals within each group are directly comparable and will react to the treatment in a similar fashion. We need to ensure that all samples are representative of the true population. For example, if we wanted to take representative samples of animal feed from a lorry for laboratory analysis, we would need to take several, at different depths, to allow for such factors as settling out and mixing errors.

There are experimental designs that are commonly used in order to ensure that only representative data are recorded in more complex experiments. Say we wanted to conduct a feeding experiment using 40 sheep fed on two diets, a control diet and one containing "SupaGro", a new growth enhancer, then it would be logical to allocate 20 sheep to each treatment.

If the experiment was conducted in order to study growth effects, it would be stupid to use adult ewes, we would use growing lambs. Likewise, the animals should be of similar weight, breed and equal sex ratio. If they are to be kept in individual pens, then they should be allocated their diet treatments according to e.g. a randomised block design, in order to eliminate any possible differences in growth caused by external factors such as pen position within the shed (heat and light availability could differ in different parts of the shed and affect animal growth).

Random designs can be generated using random numbers. Tables of random numbers can be found in the back of many statistics and mathematics books, and are available on most scientific calculators.

You use them by assigning each of your treatments with a number, e.g. 8 treatments labelled 1 to 8. By either following a line of random numbers in a table (across or down) or on the calculator, as each suitable number comes up (in our case, 9 and 0 would have to be ignored), you build a sequence of treatment numbers to use in your cages, plots or whatever.

Random numbers are usually in the form of a 3 decimal place number, e.g. 0.203. Typically you use the first number after the decimal point as your treatment number. It is also important to keep a tally of the frequency a treatment number has occurred, as you are limited by the number of times you can assign each treatment in the experiment.

An example of the possible random layout of the pens is given in Figure 9. The pen number and treatment (A or B) is given in each square, which represents one pen in the shed. The experiment is arranged in four 'blocks' of ten pens, each block containing five sheep given diet A and five sheep given diet B diets randomly arranged. Each of the groups of sheep (grouped by diet and block) should be of comparable age, weight, sex ratio etc. in order to give a statistically meaningful dataset.

Figure 9   Randomised block design

Block

1	2	3	4	5	6	7	8	9	10	I
B	A	B	B	A	B	A	A	B	A	

11	12	13	14	15	16	17	18	19	20	II
B	B	A	B	A	A	A	B	B	A	

21	22	23	24	25	26	27	28	29	30	III
A	A	B	A	B	B	A	B	A	B	

31	32	33	34	35	36	37	38	39	40	IV
A	B	B	A	A	B	A	B	A	B	

The main thing to remember when designing an experiment is to try to make your samples and treatment groups as representative of the population that you are trying to study as possible. The groups should also be very similar so that they can be directly compared with each other. If 90% of the animals given diet A are two-year-old pregnant females, but the group given diet B contains only male castrate lambs, then your means may well be different due to factors other than the diet treatments!

Randomised block experiments are good for producing datasets when large numbers of animals e.g. chickens or rats, are being studied. In experiments where fewer larger or more valuable animals, such as cows, horses or modified animals (e.g. cannulated), are being used, then you may find that you do not have enough animals at your disposal to employ such an experimental design. You may also have animals of different ages and weights that you have to use. In such cases of restriction an experimental design called the 'Latin Square' is often used. This is where each subject receives each treatment once according to a predetermined sequence, and the individual response is recorded. This method is useful in observing the mean response to a treatment between very different subjects, and eliminates the variation that would otherwise be observed within and between groups due to low replication (low numbers of subjects per treatment group).

An example of a '4 x 4' Latin Square would be if we had four diet treatments, hay, silage, cattle cake and grass, to be fed to a group of 4 cows for a minimum of 2 weeks to monitor milk yield. If we conducted the trial as a randomised block, then we would only have one cow replicate per treatment and the natural differences (variation) between the animals would be larger than (and hence overwhelm) the effects of the diet treatments. Cows come in all shapes, sizes, ages and number of previous lactations, so they are hardly likely to be a homogenous group, making blocking very difficult, even when more than one animal per treatment may be available! Therefore we use a Latin Square design, where each cow will receive each diet once, for 2 weeks, to give four replicate results for the experiment. The response of all the cows to each diet can

21

then be evaluated, and the mean for an average dairy herd investigated. When looking at Figure 10, you will notice that the treatments do not 'follow on' from each other. This is because if the sequence of the different treatments had an impact on the results, you would not be able to see or remove this source of variability from the final data. Because the sequence of treatments should not be repeated within the square, and it is most useful to start from a top line of (as here) A, B, C, D, and then work out all the different permutations of the order from that point.

When employing the Latin Square, we need to be careful about certain aspects. In this example, there are potential pitfalls that could cause problems with the results. To begin with, the cows would have to be given time (e.g. 1 week or more) to acclimatise to each new diet before the data was collected. This would add another week onto the 2-week data collection period, but without such an adaptation period, major interactions could occur between the previous and current diets causing many odd results and effects on the animal data. Latin square experiments take longer anyway due to the need to move round treatments. In this case we have 3 weeks per treatment, a total of 12 weeks, rather than the 3 weeks overall that would be required if we had enough animals to do a randomised block experiment with the same 1-week adaptation period and sufficient replication.

Figure 10   Example of a Latin Square protocol

Diet Treatments: Hay (A); silage (B); cake (C); grass (D)
Cows: 1,2,3,4

Trial period 1: Days 1 to 7 - adaptation.
               Days 8 to 21 - experimental data collection.

Cow No	1	2	3	4
Diet	A	B	C	D

Trial period 2: Days 22 to 28 - adaptation.
               Days 29 to 42 - experimental data collection.

Cow No	1	2	3	4
Diet	B	D	A	C

Trial period 3: Days 43 to 49 - adaptation.
               Days 50 to 63 - experimental data collection.

Cow No	1	2	3	4
Diet	C	A	D	B

Trial period 4: Days 64 to 70 - adaptation.
               Days 71 to 84 - experimental data collection.

Cow No	1	2	3	4
Diet	D	C	B	A

Chapter 6

STANDARD ERROR OF MEANS

It is common to find standard errors of means (SEM) quoted more often than standard deviations (SD) in reports of experiments where different treatments have been used and certain responses measured (e.g. nitrogen content of wheat, weight gain of animals).

So far we have calculated statistics using data drawn from simple sample sets for experimental treatments and used the means and SD to estimate the population mean and SD. Every sample set may be exposed to certain circumstances that are beyond the researcher's control, as discussed above. The more samples or blocks ('replicates') used, the more similar and representative the collected data is to the entire population. To overcome sampling errors it would be necessary to take several samples within the block (each with its own mean, median and mode, and SD value) in a series of individual, overlapping distribution curves. If we plotted all the block means, they would give us a normal distribution curve, which would have its own mean and SD (the 'population' mean and SD). However, in this case we call the SD the SEM. So there you have it, the SEM is merely the SD of the mean generated from plotting the means of several sub datasets (samples).

The more sample means that are used to generate the population mean, the closer the curve will be to the true value of the whole population (Figure 11), even though some precision may be lost in rounding off numbers.

Figure 11   **Sample means compared with total and single sample distributions**

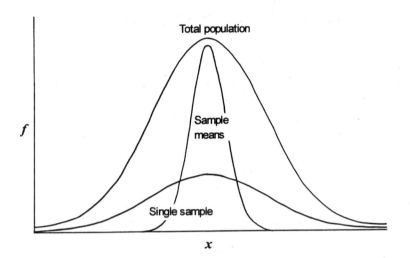

Although generally smaller, the SEM is related to the SD of the individual sample means, in that sample means with larger SDs will give a population mean with a larger SEM. Do not assume or guess the value of the SEM from that of the SD, as the values for these two statistics may be very different.

The SEM can be calculated from the SD of the sample by the following equation:

$$SEM = \frac{SD}{\sqrt{n}}$$

According to this calculation, the larger the number of dataset observations 'n', the smaller the SEM will be.

When reading scientific posters and papers it is common (often mandatory) to include SEMs in the results tables. This is useful as it allows people to use them as an estimate of variation within the experiment (kind of like a coefficient of variation). It is also possible, as we will see later on, to do a rough 'in your head' determination of whether the treatments are significantly different, and if not by how much, based on either SD or SEM values.

Chapter 7

SIGNIFICANT DIFFERENCES

So far we have dealt with methods of describing data, and have only touched upon significance, and nearly every non-mathematician associates statistics with the determination of whether values are **SIGNIFICANTLY DIFFERENT** from each other. Most scientific experiments employ at least one **TREATMENT** e.g. addition of supplement to a diet, compared against a **CONTROL** or untreated group. Of course, in reality statistics approaches science from a different angle, and tests a 'null hypothesis' where everything in a population is assumed to be the same, and probability is used to calculate if any treatment causes a true difference or not. In practical biology, however, such phrases are seldom heard.

Figure 12   **Distributions of data from three experimental groups**

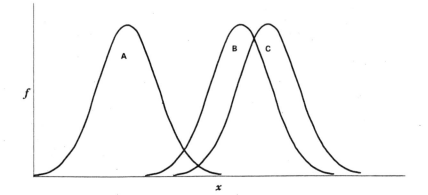

So, lets take a look at how we can measure statistical significance. Figure 12 shows three different population curves, which represent data collected from three different experimental groups, A = control, B = treatment 1 and B = treatment 2. We can see from the graph that the three curves overlap each other by some degree, A has a small amount of overlap with B and C, but the overlap between B and C is very large.

We can use statistics to tell us whether the group means of A, B and C are different from each other, and by how much (level of significance) or whether they are merely 'subsets' of one much larger population curve, and therefore not significantly different.

There are three standard levels of statistical significance (based on probability), **5%** (1 in 20 chance of the treatment effect being a coincidence); **1%** (1 in 100 chance) and most significant of all, **0.1%** (1 in 1000 chance). These are commonly written as the proportions **P<0.05, P<0.01 and P<0.001**, or as *, ** and *** respectively after the mean value. How can we visualise these significance levels on the population distribution curves, and what do they mean with respect to numbers that we will be generating?

First of all we need to decide at which level of significance we wish to test. For example we may want to find a more general trend, so we can test at 5%, or be very sure that the populations are highly significantly different, and therefore use 0.1% level. These 'levels' are often referred to as 'confidence limits' in reference to how 'confident' we feel about the difference between our treatments.

To begin we can use an example of an experiment where the effect of a single treatment is investigated against a control. The experiment was conducted to determine whether lambs fed diets supplemented with "SuperGro" grew faster and weighed more than lambs fed the diet without any supplementation. Our potential "SuperGro" customer needs to be convinced, so we have decided to test the experimental data at the 1% level (P<0.01), i.e. any random improvements in lamb weight gain will only occur 1 in 100 times.

So, if a normal distribution = 100% and we want to test at 1% level of confidence, then 100 - 1 = 99%. Therefore we need to find where the extreme 1% of all values in the distribution curve lie. Bearing in mind the 'extreme' includes the maximum and minimum values, we are looking for the top and bottom 0.5%. It has been calculated (see 'Populations', Chapter 4) that these values lie in excess of ± 2.59 SD of the mean in a normal distribution (or ± 2.59 SEM if on a sample means population curve). Figure 13 shows where these values will be found (shaded areas).

Figure 13   **Two-tailed test of significance at 1% confidence level**

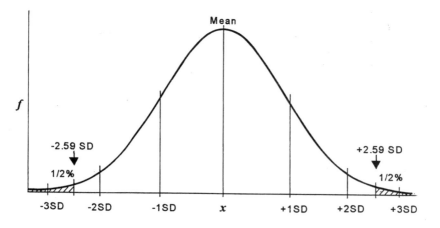

The areas where the significantly different means are expected to be found are often referred to as the **CRITICAL ZONES**. Such an analysis looking at both extremes of data would be called a **TWO-TAILED TEST** as we would be looking for the significantly different values to be present in either of the 'two tails' of the curve. The experimental hypothesis is that there will be no effect of "SuperGro" (null hypothesis – standard assumption) or there is an effect of "SuperGro". We therefore have two potential effects of the supplement.

In our sheep experiment, due to perhaps previous trial data or some predicted mode of action, we expect the "SuperGro" diet to result in heavier lambs than the control. Therefore we have given our experiment 'direction' i.e. specified what effect we may expect the treatment to have. Instead of expecting to find our significantly different value in the top or bottom ½%, we now expect to find it in the top 1% only, and entirely confined to the right hand tail of the curve (Figure 14).

Figure 14   **One-tailed or 'directional' significance at 1% confidence level**

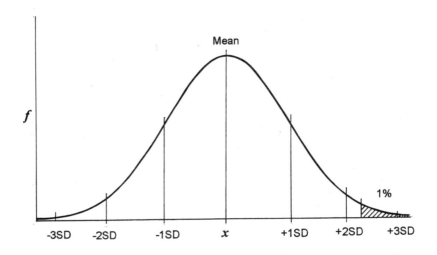

This type of analysis is called, logically enough, a **ONE-TAILED TEST** or 'directional' test, and is the one that you will often see used in scientific experiments, whereby we already have formed an idea of the effect of the treatment. Note that combining both extremes into a lump of 1% causes the SD level to decrease from 2.59 SD previously required at the 1% level of significance, to 2.33 SD (the bigger shaded area at one end of the curve). Therefore the treatment mean of a directional or one-tailed analysis does not have to be as large (or as far from the control mean) to be significantly different as does the mean from a two-tailed analysis.

To continue with the example of the sheep fed on "SuperGro", the data has been analysed, and the mean, standard deviation and standard error of the mean calculated for either group:

Group	n	x LWG	SD	SEM
Control Sheep	100	35 kg	8	0.8
SuperGro sheep	100	41 kg	10	1.0

At this point we can introduce another statistic called the **STANDARD ERROR OF THE DIFFERENCE** (SED). This measures the deviation (error) of the difference between the two means, and is a combination of the standard deviation of each of the means:

$$SED = \sqrt{((SEM\ control)^2 + (SEM\ treatment)^2)}$$

In this case:

$$SED = \sqrt{(0.8^2 + 1.0^2)}$$
$$SED = \sqrt{(0.64 + 1.0)}$$
$$SED = \sqrt{1.64}$$
$$SED = 1.28$$

We can then use the SED value to determine whether the difference between the means is significant at the 1% level i.e. whether the mean of the sheep given "SuperGro" falls within the 'critical zone' (i.e. the shaded top-end 1% of the distribution).

Critical zone = 2.33 SEM higher than the mean to be significantly different from the control.

$$= critical\ SEM\ zone \times SED$$
$$= 2.33 \times 1.28 = 2.99$$

Therefore if the "Supergro"-fed sheep mean liveweight gain is more than 2.99 kg higher than the control sheep, the means are significantly different.

"SuperGro" mean 41 kg – Control mean 35 kg = 6 kg

6 kg is greater than 2.99 kg. The means of the two groups are therefore significantly different at the 1% level.

It is important to note that the critical zone for the 5% significance level is far larger than 1% level which is in turn larger than the 0.1% level. This means that the smaller the % significance level, the more difficult it is to find a significant difference. Also, due to the equation that converts from SD to SEM values, the larger the sample size 'n', the greater the denominator (bottom) value on the equation, which leads to a smaller SEM value. Populations with small SEMs require a smaller difference (SED) between the means in order for the means to be significantly different. This is why it is very difficult to detect differences between experimental treatments using small groups of subjects. Appendix 3 can be used as a guide to estimating the numbers of replicates that are needed for significant differences to be detected in experiments with a known or estimated variability (CV%) and size of differences between treatments.

The type of significance test that we have just been using is called a **Z-TEST**. We can use these fundamental rules regarding areas of significance on a population curve to gauge whether or nor two means are statistically different from each other. If they are not significantly different, are they close to significance or not at all? To do this we need to know the mean values for the treatments and the treatment SEM or SD. Roughly, for a 1-tailed test, two treatment means need to be approximately 2 x SD away from each other to be significantly different, the precise multiplication factors for the different probabilities are as follows.

One-tailed tests significance thresholds:

5%	**± 1.96 SD**
1%	**± 2.33 SD**
0.1%	**± 3.1 SD**

Z-tests are good indicators of significant differences for samples containing a large number of observations ('n'). When sample sizes are small ('n' < 30) the SD can no longer be relied upon as an accurate indicator of the SD of the entire population. It has been found that the sample SD tends to underestimate the population SD in up to 50% of these cases. For small samples there is another method that is used called the **t-TEST**. Sometimes this is referred to as the Student t-test as the man who devised it wrote under the pseudonym 'Student'.

The t-test is calculated in exactly the same manner as the z-test, but uses a different population curve to allow for the smaller sample size (Figure 15). These distribution curves are called 't-DISTRIBUTIONS'.

Figure 15 *t*-distribution curves

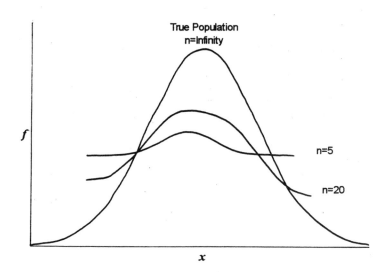

In the discussion regarding the use of SEMs rather than SDs as the more reliable description of the true population distribution, we saw how the more samples sets and sample means we generated, the closer we could get to the true mean. t-distributions look at this phenomenon from the other direction. The smaller the value of 'n' and the fewer sample means, the further the t-distribution moves away from the population mean. With reference to Figure 15, note that, with decreasing levels of 'n' (fewer observations), the mean decreases and the areas of the 'critical zones' and the spread of the curve increases (larger range and more disperse data – hence a flatter, lower curve). Therefore the smaller the sample size, the larger the difference that must exist between the treatment means in order for them to be significantly different.

Statistical t-tables are used to identify the proportion of the t-distribution versus the normal population distribution. The t-test values are looked up as a cross-reference of the degrees of freedom (df) and significance level on the t-test chart in order to determine the threshold value required for the experimental mean to be significantly different from the control mean. The difference between the two means must be greater than the t-value quoted in the table for there to be a significant difference between the means.

In simpler terms:

$$\text{Experimental t value} = \frac{\text{'}x\text{' treatment A} - \text{'}x\text{' treatment B}}{SD\sqrt{n}}$$

If the experimental t value is greater than the t value given on the standard tables, then the two means are significantly different.

Chapter 8

COMPARING SEVERAL MEANS

T-tests and z-tests are used to determine whether two datasets are significantly different from each other, yet in many situations using experimental data we may have several datasets from several different treatments, for example the four used in Figure 10 (page 23). We can still use these two tests, but if, for example, we had sixteen different treatments, then to establish which ones were significantly different would take a considerable length of time as they would all have to be compared with each other. In such cases, another statistical test is used, called the Analysis of Variance (or ANOVA for short), which deduces levels of significant differences by using an F-test (named after its originator, Fisher). The F-test would give the same result as the t or z-test if used in two treatment means alone, however it is flexible enough to analyse more complex data. It will allow for 'interactions' between treatments as well, for example if we have two breeds of chickens each fed on four different diets, then we can analyse whether there are significant differences in feed intake (a) between the two breeds; (b) between the four diets and (c) an interaction between breed and diet. i.e. whether the two breeds respond in the same way to the effects of the diets, or differ significantly in their response.

F-tests, like t- and z-tests, assume that the variability and distribution of the sampled data is normal, and not skewed or deviant in any way.

ANOVA works under the basic principle of calculating the ratio between the variance of the treatments against the naturally present background variance (the residual variance). If these two values result in a large enough ratio, then the treatments are having a significant effect on the variance.

Table 1   Example of ANOVA calculation

Treatment	Control		Additive1		Additive 2	
	Liveweight gain (kg)	$(x - \bar{x})^2$	Liveweight gain (kg)	$(x - \bar{x})^2$	Liveweight gain (kg)	$(x - \bar{x})^2$
Raw data	8	0.04	13	0.09	15	0.25
	7	0.64	12	1.69	16	0.25
	6	3.24	14	0.49	14	2.25
	7	0.64	15	2.89	17	2.25
	8	0.04	12	1.69	15	0.25
	9	1.44	14	0.49	16	0.25
	7	0.64	13	0.09	14	2.25
	8	0.04			17	2.25
	9	1.44				
	9	1.44				
Treatment mean $\bar{x}$	7.8	-	13.3	-	15.5	-
Grand mean x_G			12.2			
n	10	-	7	-	8	-
Total n			25 (df=24)			
Treatment SS $\sum(x - \bar{x})^2$	9.6		7.43		10.25	
Total SS (residual)			(9.6+7.43+10.25) = **27.3**			

Residual df (total – treatment)		(24 – 2) = 22	
Treatment deviation $x - x_G$	7.8 - 12.2 = -4.4	13.3 - 12.2 = 1.1	15.5 - 12.2 = 3.3
Treatment SS $(x - x_G)^2$ n	193.6	8.5	87.1
Total Treatment SS	(193.6+8.5+87.1) = **289.2**		
Treatment df	(3 – 1) = 2		
Total SS (Trtmt SS + Rsdl SS)	(289.2 + 27.3) = 316.5		
Total df	(25 – 1) = 24		
Mean Square Treatment (SS/df)	(289.2/2) = 144.6		
Mean Square Residual SS/df	(27.3/22) = 1.24		
F-Ratio	(144.6/1.24) = **116.6**		

Suppose we have the results of an experiment whereby three diet treatments, a control, Additive 1 and Additive 2, were given to growing piglets and the live weight gain of the animals was recorded. The results are shown in Table 1.

In this example we have the raw data for the liveweight gains of the piglets, from which we calculate each treatment mean 'x', the grand mean 'x'$_G$ for the whole dataset and the number of observations n for each treatment and in total for the whole experiment. The sum of squares (SS) for each treatment is calculated in the same manner as before, from the deviation of each observation from the individual treatment mean, although we could have used the formula previously discussed had the sample sizes been larger. Note that the sample sizes differ between treatment groups, and that this does not upset the ANOVA test result, another benefit of this method of analysis. The total of the sum of squares from all three treatment groups added together is a measure of the natural variation between the individual animals in the groups, which is called the **RESIDUAL VARIATION**, or sometimes the **ERROR SUM OF SQUARES**. This statistic has its own degrees of freedom which is equal to the total df (24) minus the treatment df (2).

The next step is to calculate the deviation of the treatment means from the grand mean of the whole experiment. This value is then squared and multiplied by the value of 'n' for each treatment in order to calculate the total variance for each treatment group. The number of degrees of freedom for this statistic is calculated as the number of treatment groups (3) minus one (DF correction factor).

The third step calculates the variance in terms of the sum of squares of the whole experiment and is called the **TOTAL SUM OF SQUARES**. This is calculated by adding together the treatment and residual sums of squares. The reason for this is that it is postulated that within all experimental data there are two factors that are responsible for the variance between the subjects. One factor is the treatment that has been imposed on the individuals within the group (e.g. diet, fertiliser or whatever) and the other is the natural variation that exists between each of the individual subjects used in the experiment.

The total variance for any experiment is therefore an accumulation of both these sources of error or variation. There are n (25) - 1 = 24 degrees of freedom for the total sum of squares. If we were to do an ANOVA of these data using a computer statistics package, the print - out would resemble Table 2.

Table 2   ANOVA statistics table

Source (of variation)	Sum of Squares	DF	Mean square (SS/DF)	F-Ratio (MS/MS)
Treatment	289.2	2	144.6	116.6
Residual	27.3	22	1.24	
Total	316.5	24		

The F-ratio is calculated from the ratio of the **MEAN SQUARES** for the treatments and the residual. The mean square is a measure of the average variance within either the treatments or for the residual (individuals) of the whole experiment, and is calculated from the sum of squares divided by the degrees of freedom for the respective source of variation (treatment or residual).

$$\textbf{F-RATIO} = \frac{\textbf{TREATMENT MEAN SQUARE}}{\textbf{RESIDUAL MEAN SQUARE}}$$

The F-ratio can then be looked up in standard statistical tables as a cross reference between the treatment and residual degrees of freedom to establish the significance level of the difference between the treatment means (Appendix 1).

Chapter 9

CORRELATIONS AND

REGRESSIONS

A correlation is the relationship that exists between two groups of variables. The simplest and most common way of determining a relationship between treatment and results is **LINEAR REGRESSION**. If it can be proven that a valid relationship exists between treatment and response, this can be used to develop theories and prove biological influences.

Figure 16   Positive linear regression

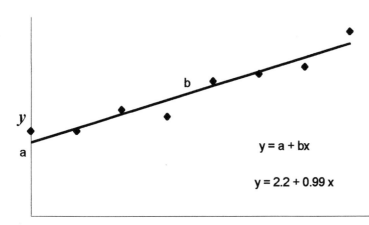

$$y = a + bx$$

$$y = 2.2 + 0.99\,x$$

Figure 16 shows a positive linear correlation. The independent or fixed variable lies on the x-axis, and the dependent (fluctuating) variable, that changes with controlled changes in x, is on the y-axis. The graph can be described using the mathematical equation: $y = a + bx$ where y = y variable, x = x variable, a = the intercept of the line with the y-axis (which may be positive or negative), and b = the slope of the graph.

Linear regressions may also be negative (Figure 17), but obey the same mathematical relationship, except that the slope becomes negative. The closer the relationship between two variables e.g. feed intake and weight gain, the nearer they get to a straight line. The line may also not be straight – it could be an exponential curve (positive or negative) or a quadratic curve.

Figure 17   Negative linear regression

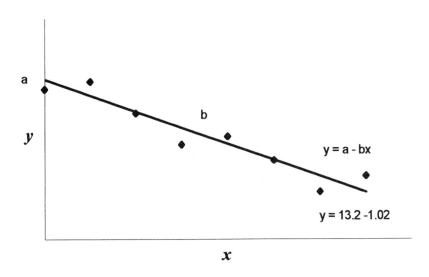

Nowadays, computer data programs can easily calculate lines of best fit. It is also up to you to decide which line is biologically most appropriate. For example most biological treatments have a finite effect. Giving a crop more fertiliser may increase its yield, but there will be a point where you reach the maximum potential of the plant and its environment, whereby no further yield can be produced, so the biologically sensible graph to use would be exponential (Figure 18). The more random the relationship between two variables, the more closely the arrangement of points resembles a circle (Figure 19).

Figure 18   Exponential relationship

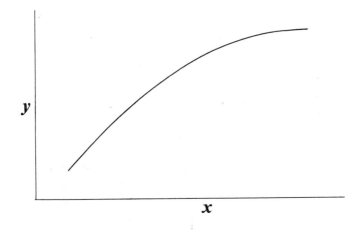

The 'goodness of fit' of the points to a line is measured in terms of a **CORRELATION COEFFICIENT** which is often denoted as 'r'. A perfect, positive correlation (all the points on the line) would have a value of r = +1.0, a perfect negative relationship r = -1.0. A value of r = 0.0 would indicate no relationship at all. So the value of r may lie anywhere between +1.0 and -1.0, however as r approaches zero, the relationship between the two variables becomes weaker. When the value of r is large, and near +1.0 or -1.0, then the relationship is strong. If the sample size is also large, then you can be more confident that 'r' is the true value for the population. The absolute minimum number of points required to draw a line graph is three, and you need five or more points to draw a graph or correlation with any confidence.

Figure 19   **Random regression**

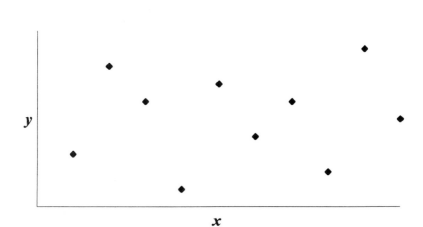

'r' is the measure of how well the two variables change in step with each other. If we have the variables x and y, then we can calculate 'r' from the following equation which uses the variance of each datapoint from its mean:

$$r = \frac{\sum(x-x)\,(y-y)}{\sqrt{[\sum((x-x)^2\,\sum(y-y)^2]}}$$

Where x = x variate individual value; x = mean x value; y = y variate individual value; y = mean y value.

The amount of variation or deviation of the individual values in the dataset from the value of r can be calculated in the following equation:

STANDARD ERROR OF r $\qquad = \dfrac{1-(r^2)}{\sqrt{n}}$

From this equation we can see that large values of r or n lead to smaller values of SEr, therefore less deviation from the value of r, and better agreement of the two variates.

What does this mean in terms of the population as a whole? Well, 68% will have values of r ± 1 SEr, 95% would have values of r ± 2 SEr, and 99% would have values of r ± 2.5 SEr, so this variance measure is acting in the same descriptive way as SDs and SEMs.

To test whether the relationship between the two variables is significant, we can look up the values in a standard statistical table by using the df as a reference point. It is important to note that, for regression analysis, you allow one correction point for the regression as well as for standard correction, therefore df = n - 2.

The size of the correlation is measured by the value of r^2. For mathematical reasons, it is accepted that the square of the correlation coefficient 'r' describes how much of the variation in the dependent variable is directly caused by variation in the independent variable.

$$\text{e.g.} \quad r = 0.80.$$
$$r^2 = 0.8 \times 0.8$$
$$r^2 = 0.64$$

To explain what this means very simply, the result indicates that 64% of the variation seen in 'y' results is due to the treatment 'x', and 36% is natural variation due to other, uncontrolled or unknown factors. If the other factors can be identified and correlated, then the r^2 can be modified by combining it with the first variable investigated. Sometimes this leads to values of more than 100%, which means that the variables are interacting with each other as well as being correlated.

Describing a regression line

It is often necessary to describe a regression line mathematically, which is the relationship between the two variables. For linear regressions this is not difficult to do. For example, if you have a graph which shows a positive correlation, whose line crosses the y axis at 17 units, and you have calculated the gradient (the height divided by the length of a given sample section of the line) of the line to be 0.4, then the equation of the line will be:

$$y = 17 + 0.4x$$

This equation can then be used to calculate values of y from a given value of x. Of course, you need to sure that the relationship is reproducible and correct before using it as a predictor! You can also use the equation to work backwards – for example if you have a certain laboratory result and you have already established a predictive relationship, you may want to calculate what treatment was used on this lab sample. In this case, for known values of y, x can be predicted as:

$$x = \frac{y-17}{0.4}$$

Other lines, such as exponential curves, can also be analysed by regression to measure 'goodness of fit' of the points to the line. The more simple of these conform to the equation:

$$y = a + bx^2$$

Modern computer software can be used to work out line equations, making life a lot simpler, although it is of great importance to fit the curve that makes biological sense rather than the one the computer tells us is the 'best fit'.

Chapter 10

MULTIPLE REGRESSION

Multiple regression is a highly complex topic that is difficult to get into, but many people find that they have to use it in some form during a research project, and so I have included this section to give you a brief idea of the theories behind the statistics. The minimum aim is to enable you to read a multiple regression output and decide on the validity of the results. The mathematics of multiple regression are very complex (a computer package plus software user guide are essential!), but basically it takes an original regression line equation $y = a + bx$, and adds in other variables to give the following:

$$y = a + b_1x_1 + b_2x_2 + b_3x_3.........etc.$$

where the subscripts 1, 2, 3 etc. represent different variables.

Each variable is added into the equation, and the residual sum of squares (RSS) is compared to the residual mean square (RMS) of the full model to give the F-ratio (similar to an ANOVA). The RSS is, again, the measure of the amount of natural or unexplained variation within the regression analysis. When a new variate is added into the multiple regression equation it will cause a change in the RSS. If the RSS is reduced, then this can be imagined as the dots on the regression graph moving closer to a perfect line, and the variation around the line lessening. If the reduction in the RSS is a value greater then the previously calculated F-ratio value, then this new variable is having a significant improvement on the relationships already within the regression analyses equation.

To give a worked example, suppose there are 5 variables in a multiple regression that we have decided may influence the 'goodness of fit' of the regression line: independents (x_1 x_2 x_3 x_4) and dependent (y). The statistics for the whole relationship, with all x variables added into the equation, is as follows:

$$RSS = 1.64 \text{ with 9 degrees of freedom}$$
$$RMS = \frac{1.64}{9} = 0.18$$

Suppose we are investigating how adding in variable x_5 affects the relationship between y and x_3. The RSS for the correlation between y and x_3 = 12.42. When x_5 is added into the model, then the RSS becomes 10.65, i.e. the RSS value is reduced, but is the reduction significant? To test this, we compare the reduction with the F-ratio calculated for all the variates (0.18):

$$12.42 - 10.65 = 1.77$$

$1.77 > 0.18 \Rightarrow$ reduction in sum of squares is significant and therefore the variate x_5 significantly improves the correlation.

Multiple regression analyses are often presented in tables, and these can be rather difficult to interpret unless you know what the figures represent. Therefore I have given an example in Table 3 to illustrate how multiple regression analysis from experimental data can be used. For the purposes of the exercise, say the data is from an experiment monitoring the daily liveweight gain (DLWG) of a group of calves fed on diets containing different levels of a supplement and different dietary protein concentrations.

The regression line equation for this relationship, where we have two variables x_1 and x_2, will be a combination of the values in the bottom line of the second, third and fourth column (printed in **bold**).

y = -1.250 + (0.0423 x supplement level) + (0.0982 x dietary protein)

Again the intercept is where the graph crosses the y-axis (usually the start of the line extrapolated back to x = 0). The line of values highlighted in *italics* in Table 3 is the intercept and regression coefficient for the whole model, i.e. with all x variables used added

Table 3   **Example of multiple regression analysis results**

Dependent variable y	Intercept (± SE)	Regression coefficients (± SE)		Standard Error of observations	% variance accounted for
		Additive (g/100g) x_1	Dietary Protein (g/100g) x_2		
DLWG (kg)	0.2284 (±0.078)	0.00536 (±0.00285)	-	0.0226	58
	-1.250 (±0.456)	0.00423 (±0.00276)	0.0982 (±0.0315)	0.0103	89

DF = 3 (n - (2 + 1 for each x variate))

into the model, and this represents our yardstick against which we monitor any reduction in value due to the x variate added in. The regression coefficients in **bold** type under the 'Supplement' and 'Dietary Protein' columns illustrate the effect that adding in each of these variates has upon the regression line. The 'Standard Error of observations' is the equivalent to the RSS. The top value is for the model without the dietary protein taken into account, and the bottom value for all variates added into the model. As you can see, the value is reduced when protein is taken into consideration along with supplement addition.

The final column gives the correlation coefficients as '% variance accounted for', again the top one is for the model where only level of supplement has been correlated to daily liveweight gain, and the bottom value is where dietary protein is added into this model. The '% variance accounted for' is closely related to r^2, but is not absolutely the same (it is important to remember this point). It is a measure of the amount of variance that is due to the treatment, by the calculation of the ratio of the total and the residual (unexplained) variance. The value is expressed as a percentage, and calculated by the following equation:

% VARIANCE ACCOUNTED FOR (%VAF) =

$$100 \times \frac{(1 - RMS)}{TMS}$$

RMS = residual mean square
TMS = total mean square

The % VAF was improved (nearer to 100) by the addition of the dietary protein values, which therefore exerts an important influence on the growth of the animal.

If we want to get even more information from the output, we can estimate the relative effects that each variable exerts on the value of y, the dependent variable. In this example, the coefficient for protein is 0.0982. If, in the experiment, we had varied the protein content of the diet from 10 to 15g/100g, then if we wanted to predict the intercept value of animals fed on a diet containing 8 g protein/100g, it would have altered the intercept value by (0.0982 x 8) = 0.786, and decreased the liveweight gain of the calves by the same value.

Please do not worry too much if this is starting to confuse you, because we are now in the last section! I think that the best advice regarding multiple regression is don't try to understand all the mathematics, just ensure you can interpret the final figures. The hardest part of multiple regression is making valid choices for selection of the variates you want to add into your model. Make sure that you can interpret what your results are telling you, and that you can link this to some scientific model, or biologically meaningful theory that you have already considered.

Chapter 11

IMPROVING STATISTICAL SKILLS

The best way to improve your statistical ability is by practice. The best statisticians tend to be those who have large experience of statistics in many types of situations. When you are next confronted with data to analyse, or a report with statistics in it, try to work out where the figures come from, and more importantly, what they represent and their meaning. There is a big danger within statistics to be tempted to produce more and more numbers, and to put absolute faith into what they represent. Statistics are often only as good as the basic theory behind the experiment, and it is important to know when to stop analysing the data. Modern day use of computers contributes greatly to this problem, as there is now instant access to many complex statistical analyses, literally at the press of a key.

The main aim of this book has been to help you understand your figures, and where they come from – which will go a long way in helping you use statistics correctly, and will also win you admiration from your peers. Your conclusions must all make scientific sense before anything else, because statistics is also a science of interpretation. We could probably correlate broiler weight gain with number of squawks per bird per day if we tried hard enough, however we all know this to be biologically ridiculous. It is especially important to remember this when you are desperate to find that significant correlation in your figures from that project you have worked so hard on for so long. Keep an open but logical mind.

One of the greatest problems you will encounter when using other references and statistics books is that individual authors tend to use different Greek symbols and notation, or even alternative calculations to work out statistical values. Unfortunately, there appears to be no way around this. Even different statistics packages for computers use varying methods of analysis. Be warned.

I hope that this little book has helped in some way to improve your statistical awareness, and that it has reduced any fears you had in your ability to interpret data. Sources of information used in this review are listed in the reference section opposite. The 'New Scientist' publications are very useful further reading material as they are well illustrated and fairly easy to read. Tables for evaluating levels of significance can be found in the back of most statistical textbooks, but have also been reproduced in the Appendices following the reference section.

References and Further Reading

*Suggested further reading

*Clegg, F. (1990). *Simple Statistics.* Cambridge University Press, England.

Mead, R. & Curnow, R.N. (1983*). Statistical Methods In Agriculture and Experimental Biology.* Chapman & Hall, London, England.

Parker, R.E. (1979). *Introductory Statistics for Biologists.* (Second Edition). Edward Arnold, London, England.

*Rowntree, D. (1981). *Statistics Without Tears.* Penguin Books, Middlesex, England.

Snedecor, G.W. & Cochran, W.G. (1989). *Statistical Methods* (Eighth edition). Iowa State University Press. Ames. P. 104.

*Stewart, I. (1990). *Risky Business.* Inside Science No. 33. New Scientist Publications, IPC Magazines, London, England.

*Stewart, I. (1993). *Testing Hypotheses.* Inside Science No. 67. New Scientist Publications, IPC Magazines, London, England.

*Stewart, I. (1993). *What is Statistics?* Inside Science No. 61. New Scientist Publications, IPC Magazines, London, England.

*Stewart, I. (1994). *Statistical Modelling.* Inside Science No. 74. New Scientist Publications, IPC Magazines, London, England.

*Stewart, I. (1995). *Statistical Sampling.* Inside Science No. 82. New Scientist Publications, IPC Magazines, London, England.

*Stewart, I. (1996). *Analysis of Variance.* Inside Science No. 91. New Scientist Publications, IPC Magazines, London, England.

Appendix 1

F-RATIO TABLES

To assess the significance of the F-ratio statistics, look up DF for treatment (n1 across) versus DF residual (n2 down side) on each of the tables and determine which yours falls into e.g. (**bold**) F-ratio of 6.91 with treatment DF = 8 and residual DF = 12, ratio is higher than value at 1%, but lower than value at 0.1% levels (P<0.01 & 0.001 respectively). Therefore, treatments are significantly different at the P<0.01 level.

P<0.05 (5% confidence)

n2 \ n1	1	2	3	4	5	6	7	8	10	12	24
2	18.5	19.0	19.2	19.2	19.3	19.3	19.4	19.4	19.4	19.4	19.5
3	10.1	9.55	9.28	9.12	9.01	8.94	8.89	8.85	8.79	8.74	8.64
4	7.71	6.94	6.59	6.39	6.26	6.16	6.09	6.04	5.96	5.91	5.77
5	6.61	5.79	5.41	5.19	5.05	4.95	4.88	4.82	4.74	4.68	4.53
6	5.99	5.14	4.76	4.53	4.39	4.28	4.21	4.15	4.06	4.00	3.84
7	5.59	4.74	4.35	4.12	3.97	3.87	3.79	3.73	3.64	3.57	3.41
8	5.32	4.46	4.07	3.84	3.69	3.58	3.50	3.44	3.35	3.28	3.12
9	5.12	4.26	3.86	3.63	3.48	3.37	3.29	3.23	3.14	3.07	2.90
10	4.96	4.10	3.71	3.48	3.33	3.22	3.14	3.07	2.98	2.91	2.74
12	4.75	3.89	3.49	3.26	3.11	3.00	2.91	2.85	2.75	2.69	2.51
15	4.54	3.68	3.29	3.06	2.90	2.79	2.71	2.64	2.54	2.48	2.29
20	4.35	3.49	3.10	2.87	2.71	2.60	2.51	2.45	2.35	2.28	2.08
24	4.26	3.40	3.01	2.78	2.62	2.51	2.42	2.36	2.25	2.18	1.98
30	4.17	3.32	2.92	2.69	2.53	2.42	2.33	2.27	2.16	2.09	1.89
40	4.08	3.23	2.84	2.61	2.45	2.34	2.25	2.18	2.08	2.00	1.79
60	4.00	3.15	2.76	2.53	2.37	2.25	2.17	2.10	1.99	1.92	1.70

P<0.01 (1% confidence)

n2 \ n1	1	2	3	4	5	6	7	8	10	12	24
2	98.5	99.0	99.2	99.2	99.3	99.3	99.4	99.4	99.4	99.4	99.5
3	34.1	30.8	29.5	28.7	28.2	27.9	27.7	27.5	27.2	27.1	26.6
4	21.2	18.0	16.7	16.0	15.5	15.2	15.0	14.8	14.5	14.4	13.9
5	16.3	13.3	12.1	11.4	11.0	10.7	10.5	10.3	10.1	9.89	9.47
6	13.7	11.0	9.78	9.15	8.75	8.47	8.26	8.10	7.87	7.72	7.31
7	12.3	9.55	8.45	7.85	7.46	7.19	6.99	6.84	6.62	6.47	6.07
8	11.3	8.65	7.59	7.01	6.63	6.37	6.18	6.03	5.81	5.67	5.28
9	10.6	8.02	6.99	6.42	6.06	5.80	5.61	5.47	5.26	5.11	4.73
10	10.0	7.56	6.55	5.99	5.64	5.39	5.20	5.06	4.85	4.71	4.33
12	9.33	6.93	5.95	5.41	5.06	4.82	4.64	**4.50**	4.30	4.16	3.78
15	8.68	6.36	5.42	4.89	4.56	4.32	4.14	4.00	3.80	3.67	3.29
20	8.10	5.85	4.94	4.43	4.10	3.87	3.70	3.56	3.37	3.23	2.86
24	7.82	5.61	4.72	4.22	3.90	3.67	3.50	3.36	3.17	3.03	2.66
30	7.56	5.39	4.51	4.02	3.70	3.47	3.30	3.17	2.98	2.84	2.47
40	7.31	5.18	4.31	3.83	3.51	3.29	3.12	2.99	2.80	2.66	2.29
60	7.08	4.98	4.13	3.65	3.34	3.12	2.95	2.82	2.63	2.50	2.12

P<0.001 (0.1% confidence)

n2	n1 1	2	3	4	5	6	7	8	10	12	24
2	999	999	999	999	999	999	999	999	999	999	1000
3	167	149	141	137	135	133	132	131	129	128	126
4	74.1	61.3	56.2	53.4	51.7	50.5	49.7	49.0	48.1	47.4	45.8
5	47.2	37.1	33.2	31.1	29.8	28.8	28.2	27.7	26.9	26.4	25.1
6	35.5	27.0	23.7	21.9	20.8	20.0	19.5	19.0	18.4	18.0	16.9
7	29.3	21.7	18.8	17.2	16.2	15.5	15.0	14.6	14.1	13.7	12.7
8	25.4	18.5	15.8	14.4	13.5	12.9	12.4	12.1	11.5	11.2	10.3
9	22.9	16.4	13.9	12.6	11.7	11.1	10.7	10.4	9.87	9.57	8.72
10	21.0	14.9	12.6	11.3	10.5	9.93	9.52	9.20	8.74	8.44	7.64
12	18.6	13.0	10.8	9.63	8.89	8.38	8.00	<u>7.71</u>	7.29	7.00	6.25
15	16.6	11.3	9.34	8.25	7.57	7.09	6.74	6.47	6.08	5.81	5.10
20	14.8	9.95	8.10	7.10	6.46	6.02	5.69	5.44	5.08	4.82	4.15
24	14.0	9.34	7.55	6.59	5.98	5.55	5.23	4.99	4.64	4.39	3.74
30	13.3	8.77	7.05	6.12	5.53	5.12	4.82	4.58	4.24	4.00	3.36
40	12.6	8.25	6.59	5.70	5.13	4.73	4.44	4.21	3.87	3.64	3.01
60	12.0	7.77	6.17	5.31	4.76	4.37	4.09	3.86	3.54	3.32	2.69

Adapted from R.E. Parker Introductory Statistics for Biology (1979) p. 119-121

Appendix 2

CORRELATION COEFFICIENT r

Look up the value of r required at the DF (IMPORTANT! DF = n-2 for regressions) of the regression model. If your calculated r is higher than that, there is a significant difference at that P level e.g. r = 0.662 with regression DF=13. This is significant at P<0.01 level (**bold**), because it is greater than the value stated at P<0.01, but less than that stated at p<0.005.

DF	P=0.1	P=0.05	P=0.02	P=0.01	P=0.005	P=0.001
1	0.9877	0.99692	0.999507	0.999877	0.999969	0.999999
2	0.9000	0.950	0.980	0.9900	0.9950	0.9990
3	0.805	0.878	0.9343	0.9587	0.9740	0.99114
4	0.729	0.811	0.882	0.9172	0.9417	0.9741
5	0.669	0.754	0.833	0.875	0.9056	0.9509
6	0.621	0.707	0.789	0.834	0.870	0.9249
7	0.582	0.666	0.750	0.798	0.836	0.898
8	0.549	0.632	0.715	0.765	0.805	0.872
9	0.521	0.602	0.685	0.735	0.776	0.847
10	0.497	0.576	0.658	0.708	0.750	0.823
11	0.476	0.553	0.634	0.684	0.726	0.801
12	0.457	0.532	0.612	0.661	0.703	0.780
13	0.441	0.514	0.592	**0.641**	0.683	0.760
14	0.426	0.497	0.574	0.623	0.664	0.742
15	0.412	0.482	0.558	0.606	0.647	0.725
16	0.400	0.468	0.543	0.590	0.631	0.708
17	0.389	0.456	0.529	0.575	0.616	0.693
18	0.378	0.444	0.516	0.561	0.602	0.679
19	0.369	0.433	0.503	0.549	0.589	0.665
20	0.360	0.423	0.492	0.537	0.576	0.652
25	0.323	0.381	0.445	0.487	0.524	0.597
30	0.296	0.349	0.409	0.449	0.484	0.554
35	0.275	0.325	0.381	0.418	0.452	0.519
40	0.257	0.304	0.358	0.393	0.425	0.490
45	0.243	0.288	0.338	0.372	0.403	0.465
50	0.231	0.273	0.322	0.354	0.384	0.443
60	0.211	0.250	0.295	0.325	0.352	0.408
70	0.195	0.232	0.274	0.302	0.327	0.380
80	0.183	0.217	0.257	0.283	0.307	0.357
90	0.173	0.205	0.242	0.267	0.290	0.338
100	0.164	0.195	0.230	0.254	0.276	0.321

Adapted from R.E. Parker Introductory Statistics for Biology (1979)
p. 118

Appendix 3

NUMBER OF REPLICATES REQUIRED FOR ANIMAL TRIALS

The table below can be used to assess the number of animals required in a trial where it has been assumed that there is an 80% probability that the treatment effect will <u>not</u> go undetected if it exists. To use the table, assess what percentage difference between treatments is needed, and compare against the likely CV% of the experimental design. The less variance in the experimental design, the fewer animals required for a significant result. The CV% can be assessed from previous trial data conducted under similar conditions, and will depend on trial site, personnel, management and housing.

	CV% Means Diff %	4	6	8	10
P<0.05	2	64	143	254	396
	4	17	37	64	100
	6	8	17	29	45
	8	5	10	17	26
	10	4	7	11	17
P<0.10	2	51	113	199	311
	4	13	29	51	79
	6	7	13	23	35
	8	4	8	13	20
	10	3	5	9	13

M.R. Pack (1997) Personal Communication

Calculated from equations given in Snedecor, G.W. & Cochran, W.G. (1989). Statistical Methods (8th edition). Iowa State University Press. Ames. p. 104.

INDEX